D1171572

MARTHA

Opera
IN THREE ACTS

The Music by
F. von FLOTOW

Adaptation by
RICHARD LERT

The English Libretto by
VICKI BAUM
and
ANN RONELL

G. SCHIRMER, Inc.
New York

DRAMATIS PERSONAE

LADY HARRIET DURHAM ("Martha")......... *Lady-in-Waiting to Queen Anne*

NANCY ("Julia").. *Her Companion*

PLUNKETT.. *A Farmer*

LIONEL.. *His Foster-Brother*

SIR TRISTRAM.................................... *Lady Harriet's Cousin*

SHERIFF.................................... *An Official at the Richmond Fair*

THREE SERVANT-MAIDS.......................... *Country Girls at the Fair*

FOUR FLUNKEYS............................. *Attendants upon Lady Harriet*

COURTIERS, LADIES OF THE COURT, TWO BLACKAMOORS, MAIDS, SERVANTS, VENDERS, FARMERS AND THEIR WIVES, COUNTRY GIRLS, THE QUEEN, HUNTERS, HUNTRESSES, GROOM, PEOPLE OF RICHMOND.

———————

Place: ACT I, Scene I—Royal gardens near Richmond
                Scene II—The Market Square of Richmond

        ACT II, Scene I—Exterior of Plunkett's farmhouse
                Scene II—The royal hunting forest

        ACT III—Same as Act I, Scene II

Time: 1712

38592

ARGUMENT

ACT I—SCENE I

The Royal Gardens, where Lady Harriet Durham (maid-of-honor to Queen Anne) holds court, tired of the luxuries of her life and annoyed with the attentions which her cousin Sir Tristram showers upon her. When she discovers a Fair is being held in nearby Richmond, she and her companion, Nancy, decide to disguise themselves as country girls and go there with Sir Tristram as their escort.

ACT I—SCENE II

The traditional Fair at Richmond, where farmers come to hire maids. Plunkett and Lionel, two young farmers, are looking for a maid to do the work which is needed since their mother died. Lionel is Plunkett's foster-brother, whose father had come to the Plunkett farm as a refugee and died there, leaving his infant son nothing but a ring, which is supposed to be shown to the Queen in case of danger. The two young farmers are attracted by Harriet and Nancy and hire them. The girls take it all as a game, but when Sir Tristram finally persuades them to leave, they find they are actually bonded in service by law. The two masters drive off with them, notwithstanding Sir Tristram's protests.

ACT II—SCENE I

Plunkett's farm, where the farmers and their newly-hired maids, who call themselves Martha and Julia, arrive and encounter all sorts of difficulties. The girls are embarrassed, they have never worked in their lives; at the same time they fall in love with their masters—and *vice versa*. After Lionel and Plunkett have gone to sleep, Sir Tristram appears and helps the girls to escape.

ACT II—SCENE II

The Royal Hunting Grounds, where the Queen and her entourage are roaming the forest. Harriet separates from the rest of the hunters, sadly thinking of Lionel. Yet when he meets her by coincidence, she saves her face by declaring that she has never seen him before. Lionel, realizing the game, tries to tell the truth and is arrested. At this dangerous moment he remembers his father's ring, which Plunkett hands over to the Queen.

ACT III

Richmond Square, where Harriet has come to find Plunkett and Lionel. Plunkett and Nancy tell her that Lionel, who has been freed meanwhile, refuses to talk to her. She begs Lionel's forgiveness and reveals his real rank and name (the Earl of Derby) and offers him her hand. Lionel refuses in pride. Harriet realizes that she can only win him by humbling herself. With the help of the gentlemen and ladies of the court she has a replica of the Richmond Fair built on the Square, and she herself changes back into maid Martha again. Now Lionel cannot resist any longer, and the opera finale unites two happy couples.

38592

MUSICAL NUMBERS

38592

Martha

Libretto by
Vicki Baum and Ann Ronell
(after the original libretto of F. W. Riese)

Music by
Friedrich von Flotow
Adaptation by Richard Lert

ACT I
Scene I

(The royal gardens near Richmond. In the foreground a terrace overlooking the garden with clipped hedges, statues and symmetrical flower-beds. In the background a huge iron gate leading onto the countryside. Near the steps which lead from the terrace down into the garden Lady H. is seated on a swing, which is languidly moved back and forth by two diminutive blackamoors in enormous turbans. Nancy, on second swing, watches her friend. Servants are waiting hand and foot on Lady H. Flowers, boxes, jewels are brought in to her during the opening chorus. Peacocks, parrots and monkeys are displayed and promptly refused. An atmosphere of lavishness and utter boredom prevails.)

No. 1. Introduction—(Chorus)
"Everything the world admires"

Printed in the U.S.A.

2

38592

4

6

38592

Nancy

Roy - al wealth and glam-our sur-round you, Why don't you take what's of-fered to you?

Roy - al wealth and glam-our sur-round you, Why don't you take what's of-fered to you?

Roy - al wealth and glam-our sur-round you, Why don't you take what's of-fered to you?

Why be sad, such plea-sures are bound to Make all your wish - es come

Why be sad, such plea-sures are bound to make, to make

Why be sad, such plea-sures are bound to make, to make

Lady H.

Oh,_____ please, go a - way and leave__ me_ a - lone, Oh,_____

true!_____ Take the plea-sures we of - fer you! Oh,_____

all your wish-es come true! Take the plea-sures we of - fer you!

all your wish-es come true! Take the plea-sures we of - fer you!

attacca

(Just as the women are about to retire, four flunkeys arrive, one after the other, all of them out of breath. They have been running ahead of their master's carriage to herald him in and announce his arrival. They stop at the steps of the terrace as they do so.)

No. 2. Scene and Terzettino
"Tristram, Lord of Picklehams"

Andante maestoso   First Flunkey   Second Flunkey

Tris-tram, Lord of Pick-le-hams,—Min-is-ter of Elks and

Third Flunkey   Fourth Flunkey

Lambs,—Earl with most pre-ten-tious rat-ing.—And her Maj-es-ty's Groom-in-Wait-ing.

(Sir Tristram enters, stopping for many compliments. He is a foppish swell, affected and slow of wit.)

Tristram

Dear-est La-dy, beau-teous Har-ri-et, Maid-of-Hon-or to the Queen,

11

just a thought, you know— Would a don-key-

Nancy

ride ex-cite you? Could you make a don-key

Tristram

go? Prom-e-nad-ing?

Lady H.

I am tired.

Tristram

Watch the ra-ces?

Lady H.

Thank you, no. Rides and

ra-ces don't de-light me, Such a-muse-ments I____ de-

rit.

38592

12

38592

attacca

(A group of gaily dressed country girls marching in background and singing as they pass by, outside gate, are heard.)

No. 3. Chorus of Girls
"Over hill, over dale"

18

38592

Sing and dance and play as they do- Not a soul would ev - er know. Oh, what non - sense! You o - blige me!- I'm de - ter - mined I shall go Since Sir Tris-tram thinks it non - sense- Please, dear La - dy, that's not

Tristram **Lady H.** **Tristram**

21

38592

(The garden has been filled with curious people, maids, gardeners and servants. Smiling faces peep from behind hedges. Nancy has run off the terrace and returns with Ballet. The FOLLOWING DIALOG IS SPOKEN as the Allegro vivace of the overture ushers in the Ballet.)

Lady H.: Come on, all of you! We're going to Richmond— please bring the peasant costumes from the last masquerade. Quick, hurry, bring them— we want to look and behave exactly like country girls. *(Maids rush in carrying petticoats, bodices, aprons and bonnets, and all the paraphernalia.)* And here— may I present— Farmer Bob.   *(With this she slams a funny little peasant hat upon Tristram's head after she has removed his pompous wig. He bows, rather flustered. The crowd laughs with mocking bows. Lady H. and Nancy grab some costumes and hide behind hedges as they change, assisted by the excited maids. Their formal dresses are flung over the hedges. Some girls run across stage displaying bones and hoops of their wide undergarments. Tristram is helpless as girls toss him back and forth among this gay femininity. A peasant outfit is thrown to him which he embarrassedly clutches. Lady H. and Nancy appear in changed costume, admired by the others. The blackamoors run ahead of them, capering, turning cartwheels. Maids curtsey as Lady H. waves goodbye. Flunkeys appear and open gate just as other country girls march by outside. Lady H. and Nancy join the group. At last moment, Tristram, buttoned the wrong way into his farmer's coat, runs after the disappearing Lady H. The scene ends in general hilarity.)*

No. 4. Ballet

End of Scene I

ACT I
Scene II

(The picturesque Market Square of Richmond. Gateway in background through which throng streams in and out. Foreground is fountain with stone carved figures. The Square is filled by a gay crowd, and framed by stalls and booths. Center is a platform, on which the bidding is to take place. In the front a space is roped off for the bidding farmers.)

No. 5. Chorus of Farmers
"Come, girls, come along"

TENOR / BASS

Come, girls, come a-long who's young and strong, The Fair is on! Come, girls, here's the test to show the best, The Fair is on!

(The maids enter and march up to platform where farmers have lined up behind rope. Foreground of the stage is left empty for Plunkett and Lionel, while the other farmers turn their backs toward the audience and appraise the girls.)

on! ... **they are com-ing, they are**

on! They are com-ing, they are com-ing, they are com-ing, they are

on! They are com-ing, they are com-ing, they are com-ing, they are

(Enter maids.)

Allegro

here! **Come, girls, come a-long who's young and strong, The**

here! **Come, girls, come a-long who's young and strong, The**

here! **Come, girls, come a-long who's young and strong, The**

Fair is on! Come, girls, here's the test to show the best, The Fair is on! Come, girls,

Fair is on! Come, girls, here's the test to show the best, The Fair is on! Come, girls,

Fair is on! Come, girls, here's the test to show the best, The Fair is on! Come, girls,

No. 6. Duet
"This is like a barnyard battle"

ten-der-ness and care. I was just her son and heir— Spank-ings,

Lionel   Plunkett

scold-ings were my share. What a broth-er! Well, at first I had no

choice, so I gave in—   You were friend-less, left with no kin—   But you

gave me grin for grin, So   we stick thro' thick and thin.

Larghetto

(Spoken)

Lionel: Yes, you shared everything with me— your mother— your home—

Plunkett: Yes, and the cow and the pig— but my pipe, I am keeping for myself, brother.

Lionel

Since my ear - li - est child - hood days I've found a hap - py home with you. Ev - er grate - ful, my heart o - beys A broth - er's love and friend - ship, too.

Banned in ex - ile came my fa - ther To your par - ents' sim - ple farm. Though un - known, he found there a ha - ven, Dy - ing on your moth - er's arm,

ad lib.

Dy - ing on_ your moth-er's arm.

f

(Spoken)

Plunkett: All your father left you was this ring— *(He takes Lionel's hand and looks at ring on his finger.)*

Lionel: Yes, this ring, which shall help me if ever I get in danger.

Plunkett

Nev - er did we learn his name, Nor his rank, nor

an - y-thing; But he said if dan-ger came You should show the

Queen this ring. This may bring some pledge re-deem-ing Or some wrong may set a-

40

right.　　　　But don't waste your time in dream-ing— You're a farm-er, not a

knight, Now＿＿＿ a good farm- er, not a knight.

colla voce

Lionel

Let the seed I've sown pre-pare me For the har - vest I shall reap.＿

Let no dreams of glo - ry tear me From the sim - ple hearth we keep.

38592

42

(Commotion at arrival of Sheriff, pompous with wig and cane. The crowd rush towards platform as bell is rung.)

No. 7. Chorus

"The Fair is open; ring the bell!"

38592

44

Bo - na fide each bid must be, Thus has ruled Her Maj-es - ty.

Thus has

Thus has

Thus has

Sheriff *(reading from parchment)*

"We, Anne, Queen of Eng-land, where - as—"

ruled Her Maj-es - ty!

ruled Her Maj-es - ty!

ruled Her Maj-es - ty!

(Hats off and pay some re - spect, Ev - 'ry - thing must be cor - rect.)

"—Rich - mond Fair is held each year For the low - er class - es here:

We there - fore de - cree, where - as, Con - tracts will be made be - tween Each

par - ty with a guar - an - tee— There - by, ser - vice

shall be bind - ing For the year en - su - ing." See?

46

Con - tracts closed can-not be shak- en When the mon-ey's paid and tak- en.

Got this straight?   Good!   Now,   my girls, we'll tend to

Yes, sir!   Yes, sir!

Yes, sir!   Yes, sir!

Yes, sir!   Yes, sir!

you—
Animato

38592

Second Servant *(a tall, bony, spinsterish-looking creature)*

Tritt? I can bake, sir, Fan-cy cake, sir, I can roast and boil And

fry and broil. If you'd like to serve Some choice hors d'oeuvre, I'd nev-er ev-er lose my

Sheriff *(A fat farmer-wife comes forward to bid.)* Farmer-Wife

nerve. Worth five guin-eas— who will take her? I will, sir— and

Sheriff

bake I'll make her! Now for you, Miss Bit - sy Witt.

Third Servant *(a curved, flirtatious blonde)*

I can pick-le, Wield a sick-le, I can churn and knead And

(Farmers rush forward to

burn the weed. I don't eat much, and I know I can Be use-ful to most an-y

grab her.) **Sheriff**

(Four other girls step

man. Kit-ty Bell and Lid-dy Well and Nel-ly Cox and

up and boast.)

Four Girls

Sal-ly Fox.

In the house, sir, I'm a mouse, sir, I am

nev- er ill— I can sit still— With a firm hand rule Your cow, and cool Your

brow when you re-ceive the bill.

Sheriff

This is too good, I'm tell-ing you. This is too good, It can't be true. It's too good to be true!

Chorus of Girls

(Now all the girls rush forward and beseige the farmers.)

Good at

stew-ing, good at glue-ing, Good at shoe-ing, and sham-poo-ing, Good at

TENOR *ff*

Good at

BASS *ff*

Good at

picnic bar - be - cu - ing, 'Rith-me - tic, and slick tat - too-ing, Bill-ing,

stew-ing, good at glue-ing, 'Rith-me-tic, and slick tat - too-ing, Bill-ing,

stew-ing, good at glue-ing, 'Rith-me-tic, and slick tat - too-ing, Bill - ing,

coo-ing, and ca-noe-ing, Good at ev-'ry-thing we're do-ing! Good at

coo-ing, and ca-noe-ing, Good at ev-'ry-thing they're do-ing! Good at

coo-ing, and ca-noe-ing, Good at ev-'ry - thing they're do-ing! Good at

stew-ing, good at glue-ing, 'Rith-me - tic and slick tat - too-ing, Bill-ing,

stew-ing, good at glue-ing, 'Rith-me-tic and slick tat - too-ing, Bill - ing,

stew-ing, good at glue-ing, 'Rith-me-tic and slick tat - too-ing, Bill - ing,

52

38592

and the mon - ey paid?

Gone! and the mon - ey paid?

Gone! and the mon - ey paid?

ff

(All scramble into background and disperse, leaving stage empty for next number.)

(Lady H., Nancy and Sir Tristram, dressed in their peasant costumes, enter in foreground.)

No. 8. Recitative
"Come on, Bob, why must you pout now?"

Come on,   Bob,   why must you pout now? Bob,   oh, my!—

Don't look so sour. Bob, my eye!—   There's no way out now.

56

38592

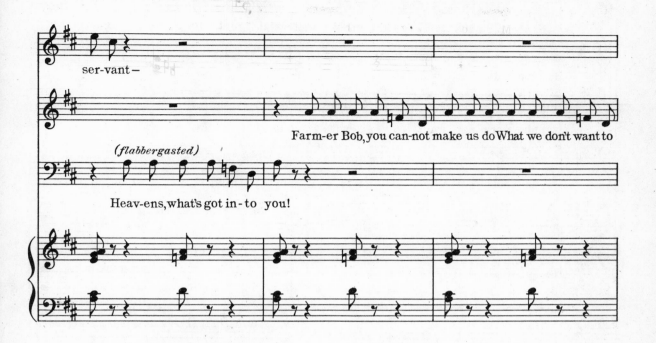

ser-vant—

Farm-er Bob, you can-not make us do What we don't want to

(flabbergasted)

Heav-ens, what's got in-to you!

I don't want to go with you.

You can-not make me do it—

do.

You can't make us do it—

Lionel

You can-not make her do it—

Plunkett *(interfering)*

She does not have to go with you— You can't make her do it—

f

58

if I do not want to go with you.

if we do not want to go with you.

if she does not want to go with you.

if she does not want to go with you. Find your-self some oth - er

(beckoning to the other girls)

maid. Girls, come o-ver here, you'll get paid. Here's a bid with plen-ty of

Plen-ty fun - ny!

Plen-ty fun - ny!

Tristram

Plen-ty ner - vy!

mon - ey.

Chorus of Girls *(who crowd around Sir Tristram and eventually*

Good at stew-ing, good at glue-ing, Good at

38592

get-ting rid of him,_____ We're get - ting rid of

get-ting rid of him,_____ We're get - ting rid of

get him, get him out,_____ We're get - ting rid of

get him, get him out,_____ We're get - ting rid of

ev-'ry-thing we're do-ing! We're get - ting rid of

(Chorus leaves stage, rushing after Tristram. Lady H., Nancy, Lionel, and Plunkett are left alone.)

him.

him.

him.

him.

him.

attacca

No. 9. Quartet
"Oh my, look the way they eye us"

Più animato

Plun-kett! Wait a min-ute— We have picked you both,

what d'you say? If you're hon-est, smart and thrift-y,

You may be with us to stay. Lionel Yes,_____ to

stay. Lady H. You want to hire us? Lionel Why not?

68

38592

chick-en feath-ers, Sweep the chim-ney— Eas - y now— You don't

want this fra - gile girl to clean the sta - ble— Clean the ta - ble!

Sev - en pounds we'll pay you year - ly, Plus a gift from

San - ta Claus— Beer each Sun-day—and on New Year's—Goose— with lots of ap - ple—

(Tristram rushes in from background, followed by maids, farmers, Sheriff and entire crowd. He throws money to them to escape their clamoring, but in vain.)

No. 10. Finale of Act I
"Here's a pound to pay the forfeit"

Tristram *(to maids)*
Here's a pound to pay the for-feit— And I'm fin-ished up with you.

(seeing the others)

Recit. Tristram *(to Lady H. and Nancy)*
But— what is this? Am I cra-zy? Come a-way. Is he still

Plunkett

79

38592

nev-er will we ev-er Be thought clev-er, Not for mon-ey or for

nev-er will we ev-er Be thought clev-er, Not for mon-ey or for

nev-er will we ev-er Be thought clev-er, Not for mon-ey or for

nev-er will we ev-er Be thought clev-er, Not for mon-ey or for

nev-er will we ev-er Be thought clev-er, Not for mon-ey or for

ei-ther, now, For you took a vow You can't get out of, Not for mon-ey or for

ei-ther, now, For you took a vow You can't get out of, Not for mon-ey or for

ei-ther, now, For you took a vow You can't get out of, Not for mon-ey or for

(During the scene it has become dark and one by one stalls, booths and street lanterns are lighted. General air of festivity. Plunkett drives on stage in wagon, drawn by one horse. He and Lionel lift Lady H. and Nancy aboard and climb on themselves. Sir Tristram makes a desperate effort to get aboard, too, but Plunkett pushes him off. They drive off while crowd cheers. All this takes place during following chorus.)

82

done, done, done, And jus-tice won, won, won.

Now the deal is done. Won! Jus-tice now is won. Done! Done! Done! Done!

Now the deal is done. Won! Jus-tice now is won. Done! Done! Done!

Done! Done! Done! Come, girls, come a-long who's young and strong, The Fair is on!

Come, girls, come a-long who's young and strong, The Fair is on!

Come, girls, come a-long who's young and strong, The Fair is on!

Come, girls, here's the test to show your best, The Fair is on! Ding-dong, hur-ry up, for-

Come, girls, here's the test to show your best, The Fair is on! Ding-dong, hur-ry up, for-

Come, girls, here's the test to show your best, The Fair is on! Ding-dong, hur-ry up, for-

get your wor-ry, care is gone. Sing-song, let your heart beat and re-peat that

care is gone, So dance and play and take your hol - i -

day!

End of Act I

ACT II
Scene I

(Exterior of Plunkett's modest farmhouse. Under a low roof an open porch stretches towards the footlights. There is a crude fireplace, a few chairs and benches, spinning wheels in one corner, farm implements. A garret window looks out onto roof of porch. To R. a low stable with half-door adjoining, against which a ladder is leaning.

At rise of curtain, stage is dark save for light of moon. Chirping of crickets and croaking of frogs are heard, then rumbling of an approaching wagon. From L., Plunkett's wagon rolls in, a lighted lantern dangling from shaft. The two young ladies have fallen asleep in the wagon, their feet dangling. Plunkett stops horse, jumps from wagon and leads horse into stable. Lantern is lighted in the stable, and through the open door a cow and a few sheep can be seen. Lionel lights lamps hanging from rafters of porch. He and Plunkett return to wagon. Plunkett tugs at Nancy's skirt to wake her up. She drops into his arms like a sleeping baby. Laughing, he carries her onto the porch, puts her down, and shakes her awake. Lionel politely awakens Lady H. and leads her to the porch.)

No. 11. Entr'acte and Quartettino
"You're home at last, you timid girls"

No. 12. Recitative
"There, girls, there's your room from now on"

90

38592

No. 13. Quartettino
"Work, work has been my passion"

92

38592

just a bit__ per - plexed, For now they won - der what, oh what they'll

just a bit__ per - plexed, For now they won - der what, oh what they'll

just a bit__ per - plexed, For I won - der what we'll

just a bit__ per - plexed, For I won - der what we'll

come to next!_____

come to next!_____

come to next!_____

come to next!_____

(The farmers pick up their things and hang them on pegs.)

No. 14. Recitative and "Spinning" Quartette
"Now good-night, but early up!"

100

38592

102

38592

106

38592

(At end of Quartette, Nancy throws over the spinning wheel and rushes off

R. Plunkett jumps up and follows. Lady H., embarrassed, alone with Lionel, makes as if to follow Nancy.)

38592

No. 15. Recitative and Duet
"Nancy! Julia! Where are you?"

beg you.

No,   I beg you,   Mar-tha, don't   go a-way.

Animato
(very embarrassed)   *(keeping him off)*

Good-night—   It's not for you—

(He grabs for the flower on her dress.)

No good-night— As pawn   I keep your rose—   I com-

Animato

(She unpins rose from her dress and next line is spoken.)

Com-mand—?   Well,   your ser-vant must o-bey you.

mand—   I pray you.

No. 16. Song

"'Tis the last rose of summer"

sun - beam that once ca-ressed you Now is chilled by the au - tumn

day. Slow - ly fad - ing,— pet - als

fall - ing To the dirge of the mourn-ful dove; So for-

lorn, are you still re-call - ing Sweet - er hours you spent in

No. 17. Duet

"Martha, I've been waiting all my life"

poco animato   *rit.*

Love is the mas-ter here now,   We know it, you and   I,____

Lady H.

Oh,

cresc.   *f*

____ My fate is in your hand to give: To make me live— or

Poco più mosso

now I know I've gone too far;   I can nev - er make a-mend—

die.

This mo-ment's like a   shoot-ing star: I can-not see the end.   For

No. 18. Scena and Notturno
"Cut this out and stop this joking"

(Plunkett races onto stage. He is disheveled, has hay in his hair, while Nancy is mischievous.)

122

Andante **Notturno**

38592

124

38592

Sweet, good-night,   sweet, good-night,   sweet, good-night!

Sweet, good-night,   sweet, good-night,   sweet, good-night!

bove you—   Sweet, good-night,   sweet, good-night, sweet, good-night!

Sweet, good-night,   sweet, good-night,   sweet, good-night!

(Lionel takes lamp from rafter and leads girls thru door into house. Plunkett blows out all lamps

save one, which he takes along. Garret window lights up and silhouettes of two girls appear. Soon

Nancy opens the window and looks out. Lady H. appears beside her.)

No. 19. Recitative and Terzettino
"Nancy! Harriet! No escaping?"

Allegro moderato

Lady H.: Nan-cy! No es-cap-ing? Are we too high? *(looking down)* And the door on us is locked. *(leaning way out)* Do you think we're good at jumping?

Nancy: Har-riet! No, we are blocked. Like a hole the dark is gap-ing— Should-n't want to break my neck. May-be they would hear us bump-ing— I am

38592

128

ner-vous— If the Queen should learn of this—

I'm a wreck. I know

(Rumble of an approaching

Oh— oh— Have we come to

two she would dis-miss. Oh— oh— oh— oh—

carriage can be heard in distance.)

this? Did you hear? Yes, it is!

It's a car-riage! Some-one comes to our

38592

129

38592

130

38592

(Tristram puts ladder down as soon as girls reach ground. They rush off R. Rumble of de-

Allegro

parting carriage is heard. Plunkett opens door and comes out on porch. He is in his long night-

shirt and carries a candle. He looks around, shakes his head as he sees the ladder; goes to stable

colla voce

door and enters. Again there is only light of the moon, the chirping and croaking. A cow moos.)

Curtain

ACT II
Scene II

(The royal hunting forest. A group of huntsmen in green coats on mossy bank in foreground. Plunkett is busy selling beer from large barrel on cart and filling mugs. In background Lionel is seated on rock, out of things.)

No. 20. Drinking Song
"Here is a fact, that's true and exact"

Plunkett

Here is a fact, that's true and ex-act— Now why are we strong and live so long In En - glish coun - try— eh?____ Yes, it's be-cause we drink but ale— Those who drink ale are nev - er pale! We En-glish can win Each bat - tle we're in With plen - ty of beer——————— if it's in here! Oh, hur-

(He indicates his stomach.)

lento

136

38592

Ev - 'ry ro-manc-er begs for the an-swer: Why are we lust - y, nev - er

rust- y In all the things we do— eh? Yes, it's be-cause our glass is

full. No one can out-drink old John Bull. On o-cean and land There's no one can

stand As long with-out fear— so_____ long as there's beer! Oh, hur-

138

38592

(The sound of hunting horns is heard off. The huntsmen scramble up, grabbing their spears and weapons. Eight men with big, shining hunting horns stand in row and sound the answer.)

No. 21. Chorus

"Tallyho, to hounds we're riding"

Plunkett

Tal - ly - ho, there blows the horn! It's the Queen who hunts this

cresc.

(He raises his mug and empties it.)

morn— Here's a toast her luck be guid - ing!

f

Tal - ly - ho, here's to the

f

Tal - ly - ho, here's to the

cresc.

f

Queen! _____

Queen! _____

(*The huntsmen exit, carrying the killed deer off. Plunkett follows with cart.*)

(Now all is quiet, Lionel comes downstage.)

No. 22. Song
"Martha"

Allegro moderato

Lionel

Sweet as a dream, You are like a dream, Quick-ly come, quick-ly gone,

Like a fleet-ing dream. But in my heart We are not a-part—

Love is there,— my love su-preme.— To my grief— to my cry, Will you

nev-er make re-ply? Fall-ing leaf— weep-ing sky, Sad-ly ech-o your good-

bye! Like a ship in de-spair, On a sea of dreams I'm tossed— Do you know— do you

care That my heart is lost? For-ev-er lost, I love you!

(He walks sadly to the background and sits in shade of a tree, practically concealed from sight. Again the horns are sounded off. Lady H. and Tristram enter from R. on horseback, followed by a groom who assists Lady H. to dismount.)

Lady H.: Leave me here, cousin, while you search for the others.

Tristram: Leave you alone—?

Lady H.: Yes, alone. I need a little rest.

(Groom leads horse off. Tristram flourishes plumed hat and rides off. Lady H. sighs, and sits down on the other side of tree, back to back with Lionel, takes off her big hat.)

No. 23. Recitative and Scena
"Where no word is heard or spoken"

146

38592

Allegro

Lionel *(having come forward to her)*

plete! It is Mar- tha— Am I

Lady H.

Heav-ens— he!

(in great agitation)

dream- ing? This grand la - dy! Mar - tha—

Qui- et, my heart, don't beat so loud.

Mar - tha— You are back— thank the

Lord for your re- turn- ing. You are here— at last you've

150

Allegro non troppo

Tristram

maid. In - so-lence, im-per - ti-nence Will lead you right in-to the

jail— Rec - om-pense for this of-fense Will be a sen - tence with-out

(Hunters enter hurriedly and surround Lionel.)

fail. Off to jail!

Chorus of Hunters and Huntresses *(all dressed in pink coats)*

TENOR

What an up-roar, what com-mo-tion Near the roy - al hunt - ing train!

BASS

What an up-roar, what com-mo-tion Near the roy - al hunt - ing train!

38592

152

38592

154

house as hired maid.

Mi - la - dy - what is this?

Mi - la - dy - what is this?

Mi - la - dy - what is this?

Lady H.

He is mad and, though he's wit-ty, Let us stop this

taunt - ing him — He can't help it, so have pit - y.

156

Lionel (He is overpow-

Pray_____ for him— his mind is dim— Fate fan-

Chain him— chain him!

Chain him— chain him!

Chain him— chain him!

ff

ff

ff

ff

ered and bound.) Nancy   Plunkett (fighting) Tristram

tas - tic! This is dras - tic! Let me past. Hold him fast, men!

(Scene played for action and drama. At end Lionel is surrounded by spears. Tristram is pleased.
Lady H. and Nancy plead for prisoner. Plunkett not able to break through the guards and help his
brother.)

Lionel

While my

p

158

38592

Ah! While this fol - ly I did blind - ly,

Ah! While this fol - ly she did blind - ly,

Ah! While this fol - ly she did blind - ly,

Ah! While this fol - ly she did blind - ly,

Ah! While this fol - ly she did blind - ly,

Chorus

While this fol - ly she did blind - ly,

While this fol - ly she did blind - ly,

While this fol - ly she did blind - ly,

What a game I have en-joyed! Heav-en

What a game she has en-joyed! Heav-en

What a game she has en-joyed! Heav-en

What a game she has en-joyed! Heav-en

What a game she has en-joyed! Heav-en

What a game she has en-joyed! Heav-en

What a game she has en-joyed! Heav-en

What a game she has en-joyed! Heav-en

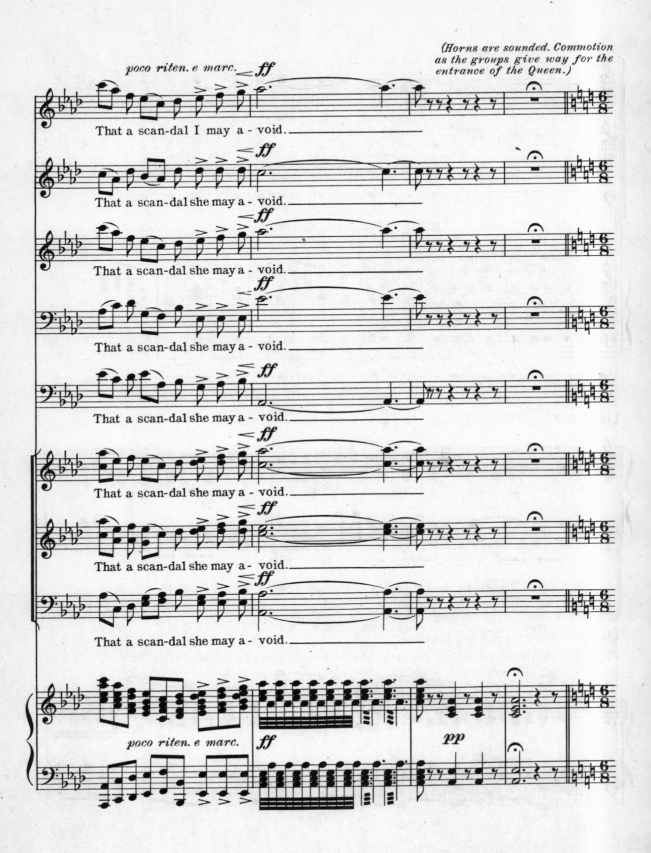

The Queen__ ar-rives,__ the Queen,__ the Queen!

The Queen__ ar-rives,__ the Queen,__ the Queen!

The Queen__ ar-rives,__ the Queen,__ the Queen!

Lionel & Plunkett: The Queen— *(Plunkett works his way to Lionel.)*

(The following words are spoken while this music is being played:)

Plunkett: Lionel, give me your ring—

Lionel: The ring? What ring?

Plunkett: Your father's ring— the ring which should save you when you are in danger— you are in danger now, brother. *(He pulls the ring from Lionel's finger.)*

38592

No. 24. Recitative and Chorus
"Quick, this ring my father gave me"

Recit. Lionel

Quick, this ring my fa-ther gave me— My sal-va-tion it may

mean— From dis-grace and dan-ger save me—Take it— show it to the Queen.____

(Royal hunting train enters in full regalia. Pink coats, shining horns and spears, pack of yelping hounds, led by green-coated huntsmen, carrying quarry.)

Chorus

Tal - ly - ho, to hounds we're rid - ing, Fol - low the call, hunt - er and all,

Tal - ly - ho, to hounds we're rid - ing, Fol - low the call, hunt - er and all,

Tal - ly - ho, to hounds we're rid - ing, Fol - low the call, hunt - er and all,

Fol - low where the quar - ry's hid - ing. Blow, bu-gle, blow— hunt-ing we go!

Fol - low where the quar - ry's hid - ing. Blow, bu-gle, blow— hunt-ing we go!

Fol - low where the quar - ry's hid - ing. Blow, bu-gle, blow— hunt-ing we go!

Tal - ly-ho, to hounds we're rid - ing, Fol-low the call, hunt - er and all,

Tal - ly - ho, to hounds we're rid - ing, Fol-low the call, hunt - er and all,

Tal - ly - ho, to hounds we're rid - ing, Fol-low the call, hunt - er and all,

Fol - low where the quar - ry's hid - ing. Blow, bu-gle, blow— hunt-ing we go!

Fol - low where the quar - ry's hid - ing. Blow, bu-gle, blow— hunt-ing we go!

Fol - low where the quar - ry's hid - ing. Blow, bu-gle, blow— hunt-ing we go!

(*The Queen rides onto stage on a white charger.*)

Racing fly the pack, the cry, "Tal-ly-ho" the

echo sings; Tal-ly-ho, for e'er and aye,

Hail the sport of the kings! Heigh ho, heigh ho and tal-ly-ho! Heigh ho, heigh

ho and tal - ly-ho! Heigh ho, heigh ho and tal - ly-

ho and tal - ly-ho! Heigh ho, heigh ho and tal - ly-

ho and tal - ly-ho! Heigh ho, heigh ho and tal - ly-

ho, _____ Heigh!

ho, _____ Heigh!

ho, _____ Heigh!

(Queen center of stage. Plunkett breaks through to her, grabbing the bridle of the horse. Guards turn against Plunkett. Queen graciously bends down, takes the ring from him. She rides off, followed by her retinue.)

End of Act II

Act III

(Richmond Market Square, quiet and empty. The sun of late afternoon slants across fountain. Lady H. on. Plunkett and Nancy enter from door of church in background. Lady H. rushes to meet them.)

No. 25. Recitative and Duet
"Soon the first rose of summer"

lone And meet him as he's leav-ing. I'll prom-ise to a - tone For all my past de-

ceiv - ing.

(Nancy and Plunkett bow and leave her alone. Lady H. walks to fountain; the setting sun glows upon her face.)

Soon the first rose of— sum-mer Will be

blush-ing to greet the day; Sweet-ly o-p'ning her heart to sum-mer, She'll be

hap-py a - gain and gay. Af - ter storm and rain be-gloom-ing Now the

38592

170

blue ho-ri-zon smiles— a-bove— Ev-'ry gar-den will be bloom-ing, Ev-'ry

flow-er, a song of love! Ev-'ry gar-den will be bloom-ing, Ev-'ry flow-er, a song of

Lionel (entering)   Lady H.   Lionel

love!   She—she a-gain! Li-o-nel—   What do you

Moderato

want here—_   fa-vors to grant?_____   A-gain to cheat me—   a-gain to de-

piú mosso

Queen, I my-self have your free-dom won. Her Maj-es-ty trust-ed

me To re-turn_ to you— this ring. She rec-og-

nized at once your fa-ther's ring. This the mes-sage I am to

(Distinct and solemn, she holds the ring out to Lionel.)

bring: Li-o-nel, this ring was giv-en to your

Lionel

fa-ther, The Earl of Der-by, Banned from Court, In-no-cent vic-tim of in-jus-tice. Oh, my

Lady H.

fa-ther! But you, his son and heir, ___ Shall be re-stored by the Queen's own com-

a tempo

marziale

mand; Earl of Der - by, in hon - or and glo - ry, You shall pos-

Lionel *(overwhelmed)*

sess a-gain your an-ces-tral land! Earl of Der-by— Earl of

Lady H. *(slipping the ring on his finger)*

Der - by. And let this ring be an ev-er-last-ing faith-ful band— With this

No. 26. Duet
"No, this hand can be so cruel"

176

38592

178

(In desperation Lionel rushes off R., Lady H. L. Nancy and Plunkett enter from L. and sit on fountain steps.)

38592

No. 27. Duet
"Well, now what?"

Allegro con moto

Plunkett: Well, now what?

Nancy: Well, now what— do you do?

Plunkett: What do I do?

Nancy: You are not a deaf and dumb thing, You must think of do-ing some-thing, Make Mi-la-dy laugh, not cry, Till her Li-o-nel comes

180

back, eat-ing hum-ble pie. And then what?

And then what? What comes af-ter that? Then what? Then a

life so sol-i-ta-ry, Just my pipe and my ca-na-ry, I'll be

lone-some,yes, so ver-y, And when hap-pier hearts ca-rouse, I'll be sit-ting in the

Nancy

Will it be so ver-y sol - i - ta - ry? There's your pipe and

house.

Plunkett

When a man is sol - i-

your ca - na - ry— But you will be lone - some, ver - y,

ta-ry He writes his o-bit-u - a-ry, And from lone-some-ness they bur-y Him—or he be-comes a

Nev - er to ca-rouse, Just be sit-ting in the house.

souse, souse, Just from sit-ting in the house.

182

38592

don't you know a slim one, Some-one who could dance a waltz?

Yes, there's

It's a pit-y, for she's

Pol-ly, she's a trim one, But they say her teeth are false. I can

pret-ty, She is slim and she could waltz, Pol-ly likes you, it's a

tell she likes me so, But for

Nancy: Where?
Plunkett: Here is where!

Più animato

Nancy
Where to look is in the dai-ry.

Plunkett
Why will you be so con-tra-ry?

Mol-ly Cow's the one to mar-ry?

No, her eyes are much too stare-y—

Well, then, who is

left for choos-ing?

You don't know un-til you ask her—

One who finds me too a-mus-ing—

be,   Oh, how hap - py I will   be! Do dee-dle

me,   Oh, how hap - py I will   be!

cresc.

_f_

do,   do, _____   do, do, do, __ I do.

Do dee-dle do,   do, do, do,   I do.

_ff_

(At the end of their duet, they run off.)

(The church clock chimes eight. It has grown dark. Now the ladies and gentlemen of the court enter, dressed in peasant costumes. They are led by Tristram, who is dressing himself excitedly with wig and robe of Sheriff. Flunkeys and servants carry in the props to build reproduction of the Fair. Everyone is busy and excited.)

No. 28. Finale
"Here the stalls and booths and benches"

190

Hon-or's chair, Oh, just the same as it was at the

Hon-or's chair, Oh, just the same as it was at the

Hon-or's chair, Oh, just the same as it was at the

Fair—Like Rich-mond Fair, the same as there.

Fair—Like Rich-mond Fair, the same as there.

Fair—Like Rich-mond Fair, the same as there.

(A group dressed as servant-maids marches in, cir-

Andante

cresc.

p

cles the Square, and takes its stand on the platform.) SOPRANO

O - ver hill, o - ver dale, Nev - er

ALTO

O - ver hill, o - ver dale, Nev - er

mf

f

lag, nev-er fail, We'll be there, At the Fair And the dev - il may
lag, nev-er fail, We'll be there, At the Fair And the dev - il may
care! We have sung on our way, We are young, we are gay, We are
care! We have sung on our way, We are young, we are gay, We are
SOPRANO & ALTO
dressed to com-pare With the best at the Fair. To a mas-ter we
TENOR & BASS
dressed to com-pare With the best at the Fair. To a mas-ter we

194

38592

(Lady H. enters at end of line and comes downstage. Preparations are finished; stage illuminated by the countless candles and lanterns. All look expectantly toward the gateway, where Lionel will enter.)

Lady H.: Quiet now— he's coming. Will he understand that this is not just another masquerade?
Tristram: Not a masquerade?
Lady H.: He shall find the humble servant he loved— will his love return?
Nancy: At your places— he's coming.

(Nancy disappears among the girls, after shoving Tristram forward.)

Animato

Will he be glad or scorn-ful, Will he be glad or scorn-ful?

He seems so mourn-ful, He seems so mourn-ful.

He seems so mourn-ful, He seems so mourn-ful.

He seems so mourn-ful, He seems so mourn-ful.

Animato

cresc.

Allegretto

Tristram *(as Sheriff)*

rit.

Start the Fair and sound the bell, And let us pray that all goes

Allegro

(The bell is rung. The girls rush up to bewildered Lionel.)

well.

Chorus SOPRANO & ALTO

In the house, sir, I'm a mouse, sir, I am nev-er ill— I

Allegro

p

198

can sit still—With a firm hand rule Your cow and cool your brow when you re-ceive the

Full Chorus

bill. Good at stew-ing, good at glue-ing, Good at shoe-ing, and sham-

TENOR

Good at stew-ing, good at glue-ing, Good at shoe-ing, and sham-

BASS

Good at stew-ing, good at glue-ing, Good at shoe-ing, and sham-

marcato

poo-ing, Good at pic-nic bar-be-cu-ing, 'Rith-me-tic, and slick tat-

poo-ing, Good at pic-nic bar-be-cu-ing, 'Rith-me-tic, and slick tat-

poo-ing, Good at pic-nic bar-be-cu-ing, 'Rith-me-tic, and slick tat-

Plunkett

dream - ing?   Maids   for   hire!   Here   is.

one   whom you'll   ad - mire.   What can

(He grabs Lady H., pulls her out from the group and holds her with a firm grip, facing Lionel.)

you do,   now,   speak up.

Lionel

Mar - tha—

Mar - tha—   you   are   here?

Andante   **Lady H.**

I can give up wealth and court tra - di - tion, I can ap-

ply for a life po - si - tion, Can be con - tent with but one am-

bi - tion: To make you hap - py, love you for - ev - er—Leave you nev - er—

Più animato
Lionel *(exaltedly)*

more. Oh,_____ heav - en's mine, For you are mine.

Plunkett

one! Wait, my girl, you'll pay in kiss - es When I'm

Con - grat - u - la - tions, hap - py pair, Con - grat - u -

Con - grat - u - la - tions, hap - py pair, Con - grat - u -

Con - grat - u - la - tions, hap - py pair, Con - grat - u -

Mis - ter and you're Mis - sus. *(All surround the two loving couples.)*

la - tions, hap - py pair, You got a bar - gain at the Fair!

la - tions, hap - py pair, You got a bar - gain at the Fair!

la - tions, hap - py pair, You got a bar - gain at the Fair!

(Children have rushed onto the stage with garlands of roses; from stalls and booths big bunches of roses are thrown.)

love, Ev-'ry gar-den will be bloom-ing, Ev-'ry flow'r, ev-'ry flow-er a song of love!

love, Ev-'ry gar-den will be bloom-ing, Ev-'ry flow'r, ev-'ry flow-er a song of love!

love, Ev-'ry gar-den will be bloom-ing, Ev-'ry flow'r, ev-'ry flow-er a song of love!

love, Ev-'ry gar-den will be bloom-ing, Ev-'ry flow'r, ev-'ry flow-er a song of love!

love, Ev-'ry gar-den will be bloom-ing, Ev-'ry flow'r, ev-'ry flow-er a song of love!

love, Ev-'ry gar-den will be bloom-ing, Ev-'ry flow'r, ev-'ry flow-er a song of love!

love, Ev-'ry gar-den will be bloom-ing, Ev-'ry flow'r, ev-'ry flow-er a song of love!

dance and play and take your hol - i - day!

dance and play and take your hol - i - day!

dance and play and take your hol - i - day!

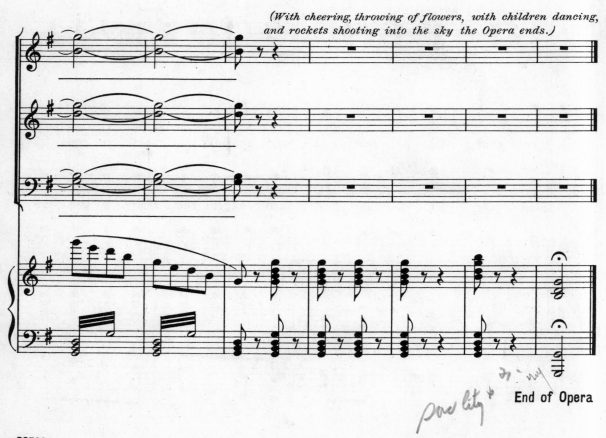

(With cheering, throwing of flowers, with children dancing, and rockets shooting into the sky the Opera ends.)

End of Opera